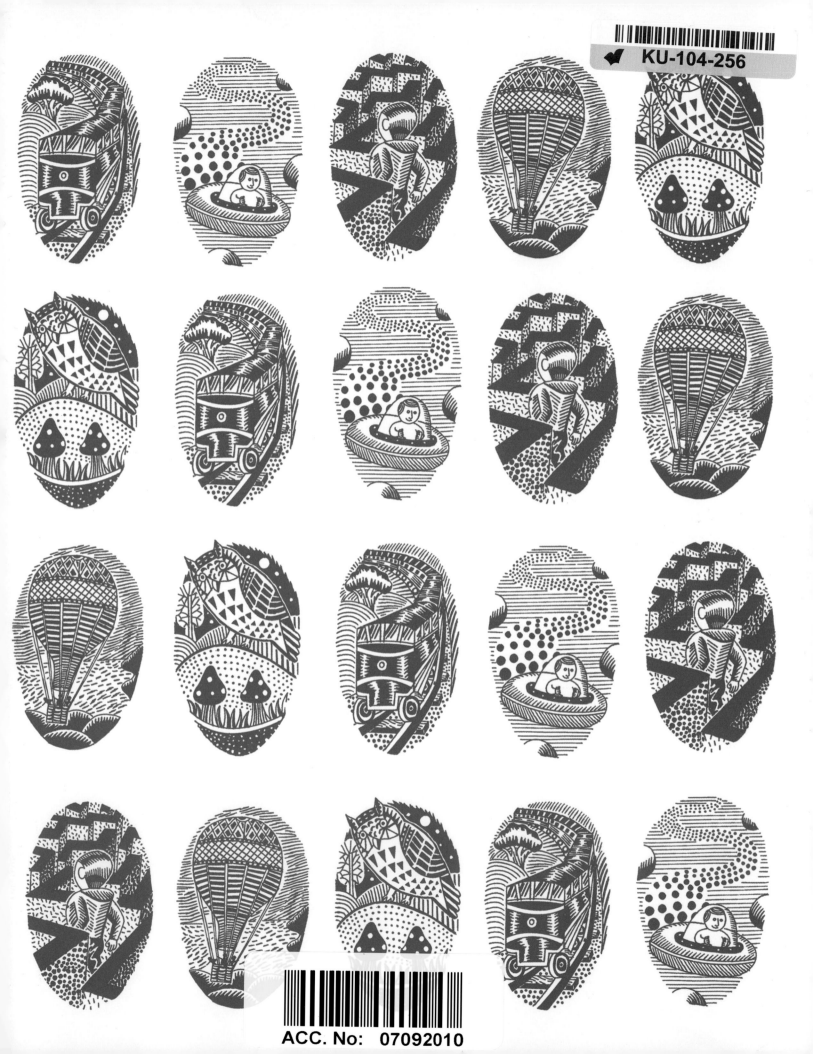

WE'RE GOING PLACES

First published in the UK in 2021 by
Pavilion Children's Books
43 Great Ormond Street
London, WC1N 3HZ
An imprint of Pavilion Books Company Limited

Publisher and editor: Neil Dunnicliffe
Designer: Sarah Crookes

ISBN: 9781843654971

A CIP catalogue record for this book is available from the British Library.

10 9 8 7 6 5 4 3 2 1

Reproduction by Mission, Hong Kong
Printed and bound by Toppan Leefung Ltd, China

This book can be ordered at www.pavilionbooks.com, or try your local bookshop.

WE'RE GOING PLACES

By Mick Jackson
& John Broadley

When you're very young
you're almost always carried
or pushed in a buggy.
You never go too far on your own.
But then you learn to roll
and crawl
and wobble-walk
and things really start to change.

Every day you're growing stronger.
You start to climb and clamber,
to look out of windows,
to make your way up all those stairs.
Every trip is a little expedition.
You're going places you've never been before.

Soon you're out and about,
holding hands.
Sometimes stumbling,
often stopping
to have a good, long look at things.

Very soon
there will be
tricycles,
bicycles,
skateboards,
roller skates.

Imagine going up, up, up
in a hot air balloon,
until it's cold and quiet.
Imagine all the roads below,
the rivers and railways —
sometimes coming together,
criss-crossing at bridges,
then going off on their own again.

Draw a map of some of your favourite places –
your friend's house,
the path with all the puddles,
that tree you climb.
Think of how you go from one place to the other –
all the twists and turns you take.

Sometimes it's good to take your time,
to dilly-dally.
Other times, everything's a mad flap, dash and scramble
because WE'RE GOING TO BE LATE!

Some journeys you just can't wait to get there.

Others, you'd be happy never to arrive.

Each creature
has its own way of going.
Moles you rarely see at all.
Some birds fly off
to stay in the sun's good company.
Other creatures hide away for the winter,
that year's travelling done.

Have you ever been abroad...
taken a train...
plane...
been on horseback?
Are you good at running?
Can you scoot?

In some countries it gets so cold
the lakes and rivers freeze right over.
Then people pull on their skates,
their hats and scarves
and everyone goes out on the ice,
arm-in-arm-in-arm.

Every minute
tiny journeys are going on all around you —
the bee bumbling from blossom to blossom,
the raindrop slowly rolling
down the window pane.

Some people like to
do things a little differently.
A woman called Annie
went over Niagara Falls in a barrel.
A man named Otto
invented his own flying machine.

What would you like to do?

In the future
things will be different,

just as things were
different in the past.

Sometimes it's good just to stop
and watch the world go by.

Some roads have been around for thousands of years.
Think of all the feet,
the horses' hooves,
and wheels
that must have gone along them.
Do you think the roads remember?
Is the old road buried somewhere underneath?

The clouds are on the move too,
slowly blown by the wind.
An hour from now they'll be far from here.

Even when we sleep
we slowly roll and turn
beneath the covers.

In our dreams
we find we can do
all kinds of things...

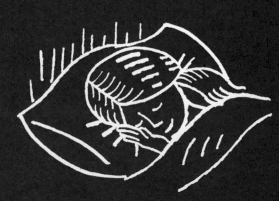

No wonder
we're so tired
when we wake.

We each make our way
along our own paths.
Sometimes we take a turning,
just to see what's there.

As people grow old
they start to slow —
can't always go quite as far
as they used to.
They might need a stick
to help them make their way...

...but they carry with them all the places they've been to,
the paths they chose to take.

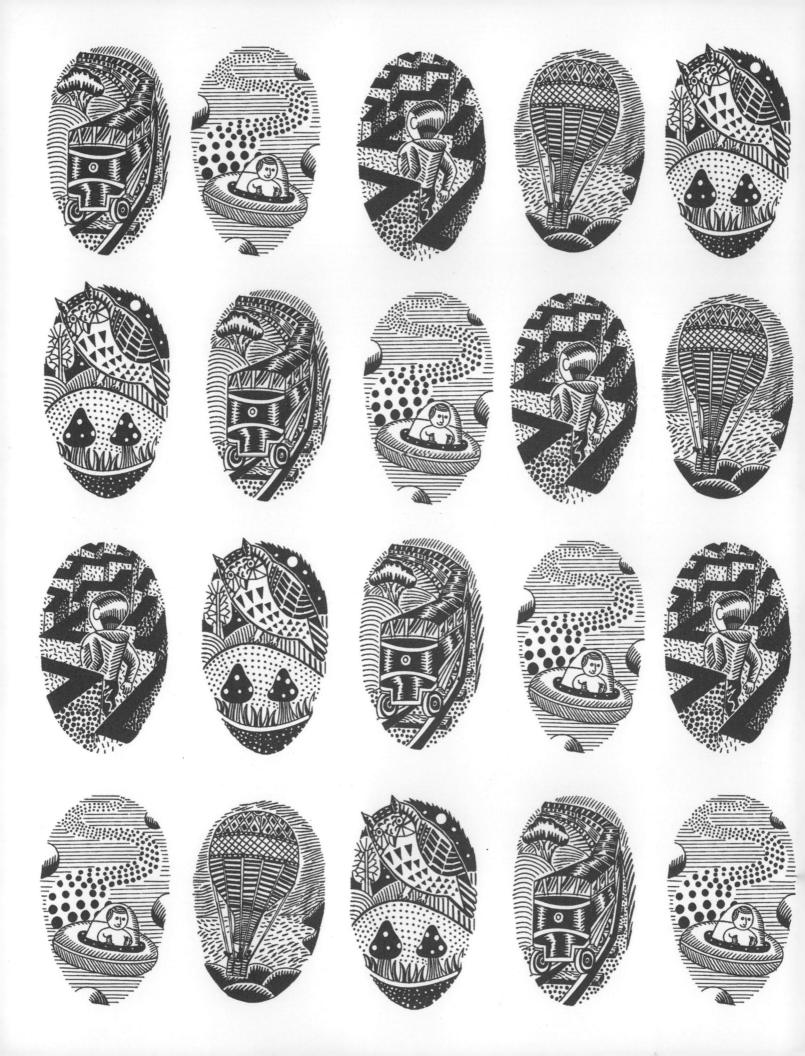